P9-BYX-395

STANDARD OF EXCELLENCE

ENHANCED COMPREHENSIVE BAND METHOD

By Bruce Pearson

Dear Student:

Congratulations! You have successfully attained the first level in achieving a standard of excellence in music-making. By now, you have discovered that careful study and regular practice have brought you the joy and satisfaction of making beautiful music.

You are now ready to move to the next level in your music-making. I want to welcome you to STANDARD OF EXCELLENCE *ENHANCED*, Book 2. I also want to wish you continued success and enjoyment.

Best wishes,

Bruce Pearson

Practice and Assessment - the key to EXCELLENCE!

▶ Make practicing part of your daily schedule. If you plan it as you do any other activity, you will find plenty of time for it.

▶ Try to practice in the same place every day. Choose a place where you can concentrate on making music. Start with a regular and familiar warm-up routine, including rudiments and simple technical exercises. Like an athlete, you need to warm-up your mind and muscles before you begin performing.

▶ Set goals for every practice session. Keep track of your practice time and progress on the front cover Practice Journal.

▶ Practice the difficult spots in your lesson assignment and band music over and over at a slower tempo, until you can play them perfectly, then gradually increase the tempo. Use the *iPAS* Metronome to track your progress and ensure you are playing with a steady pulse. Choose Tuner-Metronome as your instrument in the log in screen.

▶ Spend time practicing alone and with the Accompaniment Recordings. Make time for practice on both snare drum and your mallet percussion instrument.

▶ At the end of each practice session, play something fun!

Also Available: STANDARD OF EXCELLENCE ENHANCED Timpani & Auxiliary Percussion Book 2 (PW22TM)

ISBN 0-8497-0784-6

 NEIL A. KJOS MUSIC COMPANY, PUBLISHER

There are two ways to play a roll:

1) Using multiple bounce strokes: 
RRrrr LLlll

2) Using open double strokes: 
RR LL

The multiple bounce stroke roll is used for most concert band, orchestra, and ensemble playing. The double stroke open roll is used primarily in marches and in marching band. In this book, rolls may be played either way.

NINE STROKE ROLL (QUARTER NOTE ROLL)

written:
R R L L
primary strokes:
R L R L R L R L R L
played using multiple bounce strokes:
R L R L R L R L R L
played using open double strokes:
RRLLRRLL R LLRRLLRR L

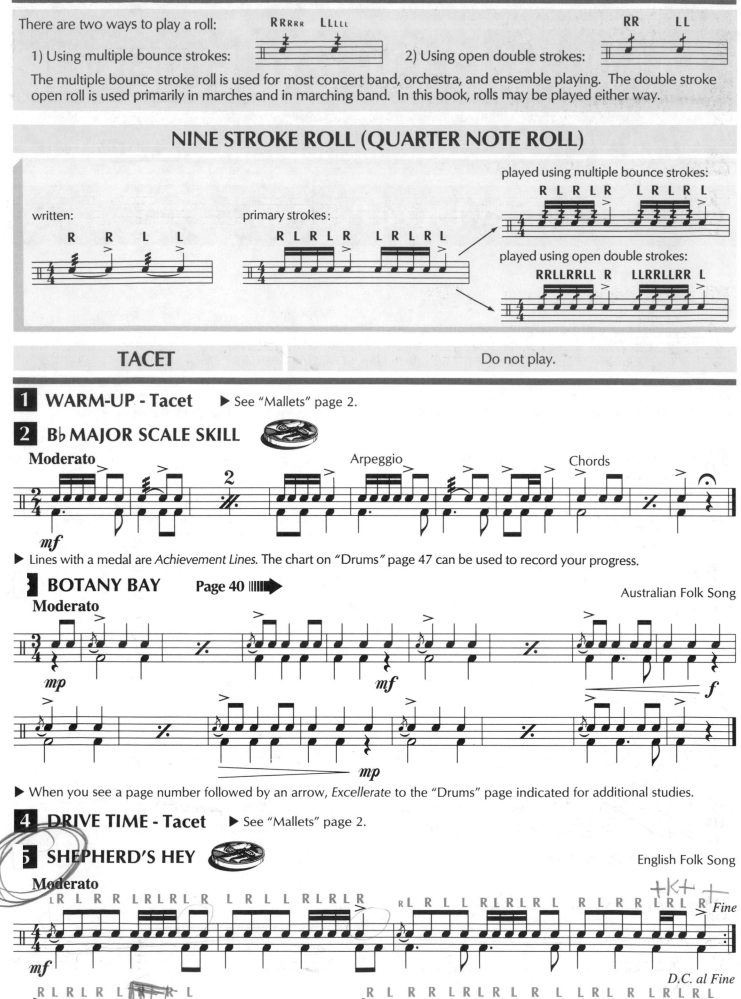

TACET

Do not play.

1 WARM-UP - Tacet

▶ See "Mallets" page 2.

2 B♭ MAJOR SCALE SKILL

Moderato
Arpeggio
Chords
2
mf

▶ Lines with a medal are *Achievement Lines*. The chart on "Drums" page 47 can be used to record your progress.

3 BOTANY BAY

Page 40

Australian Folk Song

Moderato
mp
mf
f
mp

▶ When you see a page number followed by an arrow, *Excellerate* to the "Drums" page indicated for additional studies.

4 DRIVE TIME - Tacet

▶ See "Mallets" page 2.

5 SHEPHERD'S HEY

English Folk Song

Moderato
Fine
mf
D.C. al Fine
p

REVIEW

B♭ MAJOR KEY SIGNATURE

1 WARM-UP - Band Arrangement
Andante

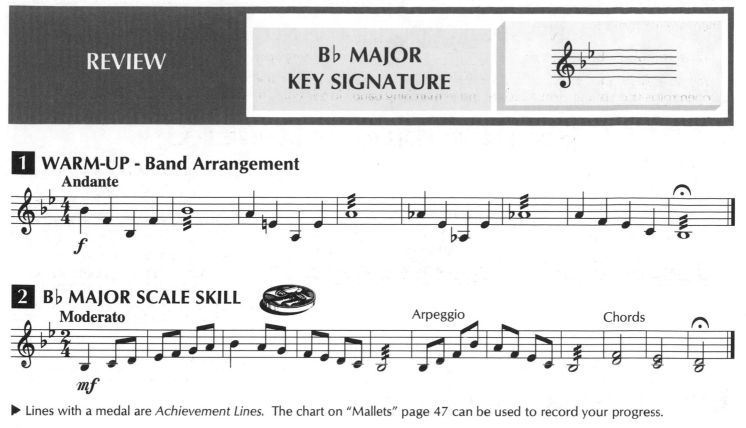

2 B♭ MAJOR SCALE SKILL
Moderato

Arpeggio   Chords

▶ Lines with a medal are *Achievement Lines*. The chart on "Mallets" page 47 can be used to record your progress.

3 BOTANY BAY
Moderato   Page 40 ▶
Australian Folk Song

▶ When you see a page number followed by an arrow, *Excellerate* to the "Mallets" page indicated for additional studies.

4 DRIVE TIME
Andante

▶ Are you using logical stickings?

5 SHEPHERD'S HEY
Moderato
English Folk Song
Fine

D.C. al Fine

REVIEW

E♭ MAJOR KEY SIGNATURE

6 **E♭ MAJOR SCALE SKILL**

Moderato

Arpeggio   Chords

mf

▶ Are you playing with a good grip and hand position?

7 **MOLLY MALONE**

Irish Folk Song

Andante

mp   *f*   *mp*   *rit.*   *mp*

8 **NO LOOKING BACK**   Page 40 Page 40

Moderato

mf

9 **TURKISH MARCH**

Wolfgang Amadeus Mozart (1756 - 1791)

Allegro

mf

10 **HYMN OF THANKSGIVING - Band Arrangement**

Johann Crüger (1598 - 1662)
arr. Bruce Pearson (b. 1942)

Andante

mf   *p*   *mf*

p

f   *mf*   *rit.*

REVIEW

F MAJOR KEY SIGNATURE

11 WARM-UP - Band Arrangement

Andante

▶ To play a double stop as a roll, position one mallet above each note and play rapidly alternating single strokes for the duration of the notes.

12 F MAJOR SCALE SKILL

Moderato

Arpeggio   Chords

13 KNUCKLEBUSTER

Moderato

1.   2.

14 GIVE ME THAT OLD TIME RELIGION

Page 40 ▶

American Spiritual

Allegro

clap

15 _____   Composer _____

your name

Moderato

▶ Compose an ending for this melody. Title and play your composition.

16 FOR MALLETS ONLY

Andante

▶ Move smoothly between the rolled notes.

SYNCOPATION

A rhythmic effect which places emphasis on a weak or unaccented part of the measure.

17 SYNCOPATION SENSATION

Moderato

mf

8 THE RIDDLE SONG

American Folk Song

Moderato

mp

▶ Write in the counting for the B.D. part before you play.

9 NOBODY KNOWS THE TROUBLE I'VE SEEN

American Spiritual

Moderato

mf

20 INTERVAL INQUIRY - Tacet   ▶ See "Mallets" page 5.

21 GO FOR EXCELLENCE!

American Folk Song

Allegro

"Liza Jane"

mf

f

G MINOR KEY SIGNATURE

G minor has the same key signature as B♭ major.

TEMPO

Accelerando (accel.) - Gradually increase the tempo.

22 WARM-UP - Band Arrangement

Andante

mf

23 G NATURAL MINOR SCALE SKILL

Moderato

f

24 G HARMONIC MINOR SCALE SKILL   Page 40 ▶

Moderato

f

25 MINKA, MINKA

Ukrainian Folk Song

Moderato

mp   2nd time - *accel.*   I ley!

26 LAREDO - Duet

Mexican Folk Song

Moderato

f

▶ Name the interval between the top and bottom notes of the last measure. _____

27 TURNING YOU LOOSE

Moderato

mf

28 FOR MALLETS ONLY

Largo

mf

DAL SEGNO AL FINE (D.S. AL FINE)

Go back to the sign (𝄋) and play until the *Fine.*

JOYEUX NOËL
Band Arrangement

French Carol
arr. Chuck Elledge (b. 1961)

Snare Drum (snares on)
Snare Drum (snares off)
Bass Drum

▶ Set up two snare drums to play this arrangement, one with "snares on" and another with "snares off."

29 GO FOR EXCELLENCE!

DAL SEGNO AL FINE
(D.S. AL FINE)

Go back to the sign (𝄋) and play until the *Fine.*

JOYEUX NOËL
Band Arrangement

French Carol
arr. Chuck Elledge (b. 1961)

Bells
Chimes

▶ To play the chimes, strike the cap at the top end of each tube. Use a quick arm/wrist stroke. For more information, see "Mallets" page 48.

29 GO FOR EXCELLENCE!

DRAG

The drag is a Rudiment.

30 EIGHTH REST ON THE BEAT / **31** EIGHTH REST OFF THE BEAT

32 ACADEMIC FESTIVAL MARCH - Trio

Johannes Brahms (1833 - 1897)

33 BREEZIN'

34 YANKEE DOODLE - Duet

American Folk Song

35 FOR SNARE DRUMS ONLY

EIGHTH REST

𝄾

𝄾 = ½ count in **2/4** **3/4**, and **4/4** time.

An eighth rest is as long as an eighth note.

30 EIGHTH REST ON THE BEAT

Moderato

mf

▶ Write in the counting and clap the rhythm before you play.

31 EIGHTH REST OFF THE BEAT

Moderato

f

32 ACADEMIC FESTIVAL MARCH - Trio

Johannes Brahms (1833 - 1897)

Moderato

A.

B. *f*

C. *f*

f

33 BREEZIN'

Allegro

p

34 YANKEE DOODLE - Duet

American Folk Song

Moderato

A.

mf

B.

mf

35 FOR MALLETS ONLY

Moderato

L R L R   L R L   R L R L   R L R

mf

36 Ab MAJOR SCALE SKILL

Andante

▶ Count eighth notes as you play to prevent rushing.

37 GREASED LIGHTNING

Allegro

38 PARTNER SONGS - Tacet   ▶ See "Mallets" page 9.

39 GO FOR EXCELLENCE!

Stephen Foster (1826 - 1864)

Moderato

"Oh! Susanna"

A♭ MAJOR KEY SIGNATURE

This key signature means play all B's as B flats, all E's as E flats, all A's as A flats, and all D's as D flats.

TEXTURES

Monophony - a single unaccompanied melody.

Polyphony - two or more melodies played at the same time.

36 A♭ MAJOR SCALE SKILL

Andante

Arpeggio   Chords

37 GREASED LIGHTNING

Allegro

mf

38 PARTNER SONGS - Duet

Moderato

A. *"White Coral Bells"*   Traditional

mf

B. *"Vespers Song"*   Russian Air

mf

▶ For an example of monophony, play line A or line B alone. For an example of polyphony, play line A while someone else plays line B.

39 GO FOR EXCELLENCE!

Stephen Foster (1826 - 1864)

Moderato

"Oh! Susanna"

mp

f   *mp* *accel.*

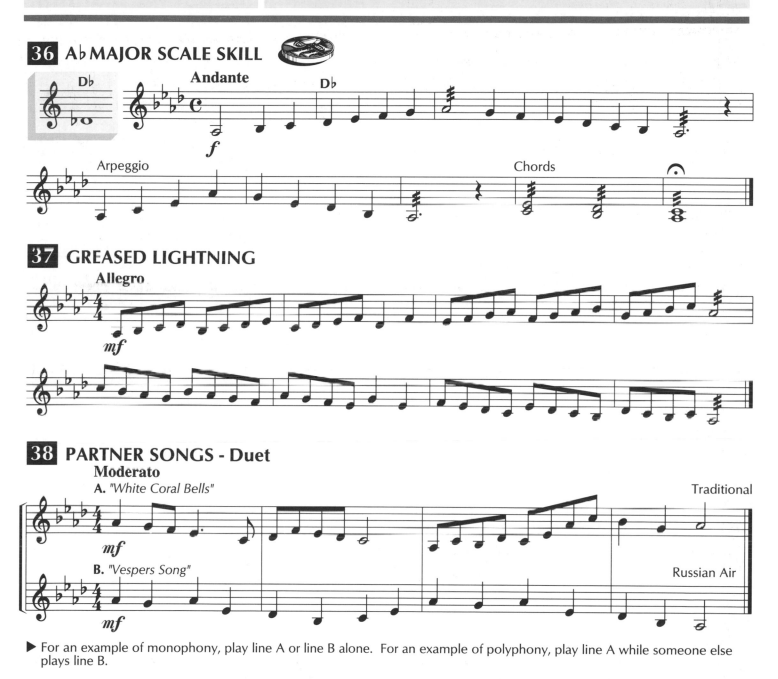

SINGLE DRAG TAP

The single drag tap is a Rudiment.

TEMPO

Allegretto - light and lively; slightly slower than **Allegro.**

40 **WARM-UP - Tacet** ▶ See "Mallets" page 10.

41 **CHROMATIC CAPERS** Page 40 ▶

Moderato

42 **SHENANDOAH** American Folk Song

Andante

43 **THEME FROM SYMPHONY NO. 94 - Tacet** ▶ See "Mallets" page 10.

44 **PARADE OF THE TIN SOLDIERS** Léon Jessel (1871 - 1942)

Allegretto

45 **FOR DRUMS ONLY** Page 40 ▶

Moderato

▶ Play each pattern several times. The S. Cym. and S.D. parts should be played by one percussionist. Advanced percussionists may also try playing all parts, including the B.D. part, on drum set.

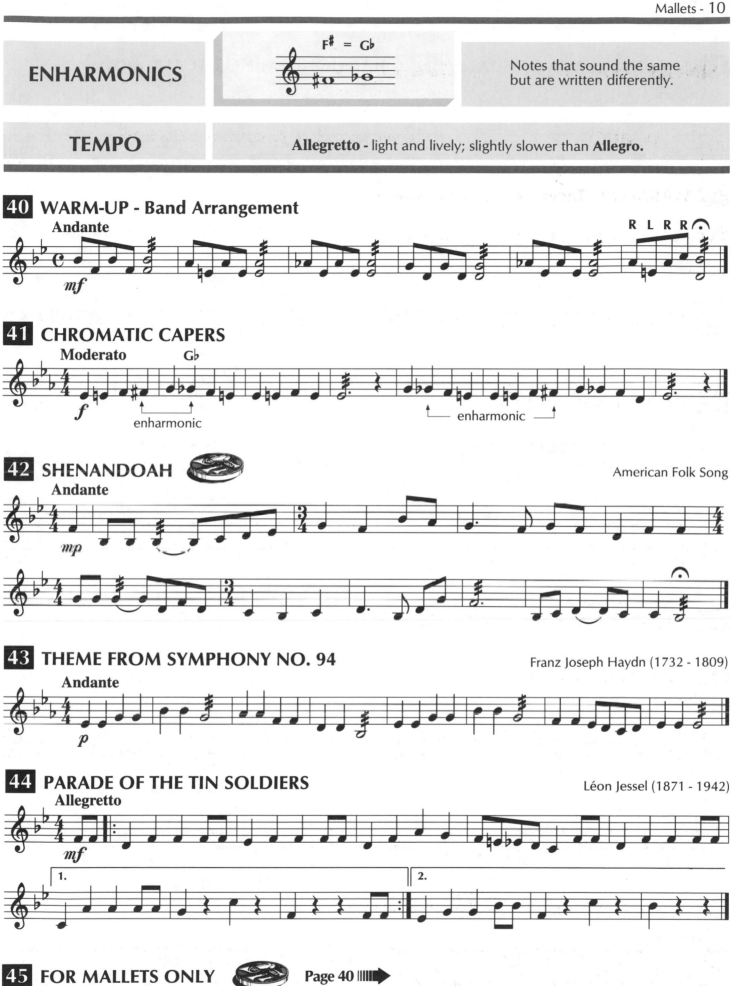

46 C NATURAL MINOR SCALE / **47** C HARMONIC MINOR SCALE

48 MARCHE SLAV

Peter Ilyich Tchaikovsky (1840 - 1893)

49 GREENSLEEVES

English Song

▶ Are you playing with a good posture and grip?

50 JUBILATE

Wolfgang Amadeus Mozart (1756 - 1791)

51 GO FOR EXCELLENCE!

C MINOR KEY SIGNATURE

C minor has the same key signature as E♭ major.

ARTICULATION

legato

Legato - Play as smoothly as possible.

46 C NATURAL MINOR SCALE

Andante

mf

47 C HARMONIC MINOR SCALE

B

Andante

B

mf

48 MARCHE SLAV

Peter Ilyich Tchaikovsky (1840 - 1893)

Andante

mf legato

1.

2.

49 GREENSLEEVES

English Song

B   G

Moderato

B

mp legato

G

▶ Name the key in "Greensleeves." _____

50 JUBILATE

Wolfgang Amadeus Mozart (1756 - 1791)

Allegretto

mf

>

>

>

1.

2.

51 GO FOR EXCELLENCE!

Allegretto

mf

52 WARM-UP

Andante

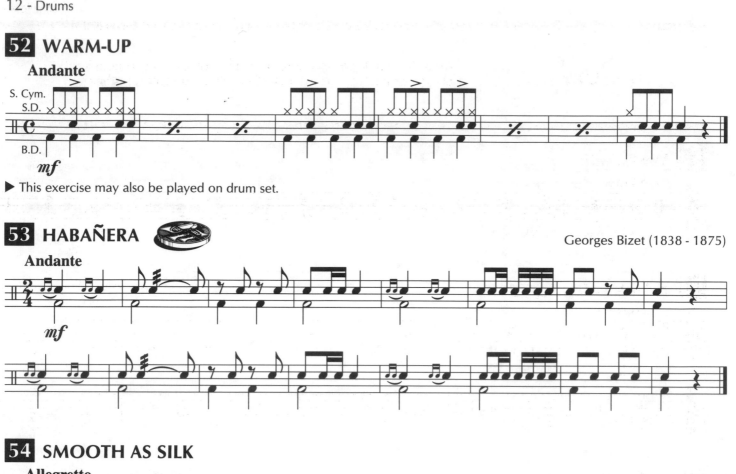

▶ This exercise may also be played on drum set.

53 HABAÑERA

Georges Bizet (1838 - 1875)

Andante

54 SMOOTH AS SILK

Allegretto

55 HEY HO - Round (Canon)

Medieval Song

Allegro

56 THE BRITISH GRENADIERS - Tacet ▶ See "Mallets" page 12.

57 FOR DRUMS ONLY Page 40

Moderato

▶ This exercise may also be played on drum set.

TEXTURE

Melody and Accompaniment - main melody is accompanied by chords or less important melodies called **countermelodies.**

52 **WARM-UP**

Andante

mf legato

53 **HABAÑERA**

Georges Bizet (1838 - 1875)

Andante

mf

54 **SMOOTH AS SILK**

Allegretto

f

55 **HEY HO - Round (Canon)**

Medieval Song

Allegro

1. 2. 3.

f

56 **THE BRITISH GRENADIERS - Duet**

English Folk Song

Allegro

A. Melody

f

B. Countermelody

f

57 **FOR MALLETS ONLY**

Andante

R.H.

L.H.

mf

TIME SIGNATURE

This time signature is called **cut time** or *alla breve*.

¢ = 2/2 = 2 counts in each measure
2/2 = half note gets 1 count

58 CUT AND PASTE

Moderato

mf

▶ Write in the counting and clap the rhythm before you play.

59 OATS, PEAS, BEANS

American Folk Song

Moderato

A. S.D. (snares on)

mf

B. S.D. (snares off)

mf

60 THE VICTORS

Fight Song

Allegro

f

61 OVER EASY

Andante

f

62 GO FOR EXCELLENCE!

John Philip Sousa (1854 - 1932)

Allegretto

"High School Cadets March"

mp

mf

f

mp

ENHARMONICS

C♯ = D♭

CHORD

fifth
third
root

Two or more pitches sounded at the same time.

63 WARM-UP - Band Arrangement

Andante

C♯

mf

64 DANISH ROLL

Danish Folk Song

Moderato

Fine

mp

D.C. al Fine

f

65 RUSSIAN SAILORS' DANCE

Reinhold Glière (1875 - 1956)

Allegretto

f

Fine

mf

D.C. al Fine

66 CHORD CAPERS

major chord ————————————— minor chord

▶ Listen for the different types of chords played by the full band. The mallets are playing two notes of each chord.

67 FOR MALLETS ONLY Page 41 ▶

A   B♭

Andante
A   B♭

mf

68 CHROMATIC SCALE SKILL

▶ This exercise may also be played on drum set.

69 SAILING THE HIGH SEAS

70 CHROMATIC MARCH

71 MANHATTAN BEACH MARCH

John Philip Sousa (1854 - 1932)

72 GO FOR EXCELLENCE! Page 41

▶ This exercise may also be played on drum set.

DA CAPO AL CODA (D.C. AL CODA)

Go back to the beginning and play until the coda sign (⊕). When you reach the coda sign, skip to the *Coda* (⊕).

— Suspended Cymbal
— Snare Drum (snares on)
— Snare Drum (snares off)
— Bass Drum

ROCK ISLAND EXPRESS
Band Arrangement

Chuck Elledge (b. 1961)

▶ Set up two snare drums to play this piece, one with "snares on" and another with "snares off." The S. Cym. and two S.D. parts should be played by one percussionist. Advanced percussionists may also try playing all parts, including the B.D. part, on drum set.

DA CAPO AL CODA
(D.C. AL CODA)

Go back to the beginning and play until the coda sign (⊕). When you reach the coda sign, skip to the *Coda* (⊕).

ROCK ISLAND EXPRESS
Band Arrangement

Chuck Elledge (b. 1961)

Bells

TIME SIGNATURE

$\begin{matrix} 3 \\ 8 \end{matrix}$

3 = 3 counts in each measure
8 = eighth note gets 1 count

73 **Tacet** ▶ See "Mallets" page 17.

74 TRIPLE PLAY

Allegretto

A.

B.

▶ Write in the counting and clap the rhythm before you play.

75 WE THREE KINGS   John H. Hopkins, Jr. (1820 - 1891)

Andante

76 GO FOR EXCELLENCE!

Allegro

TIME SIGNATURE

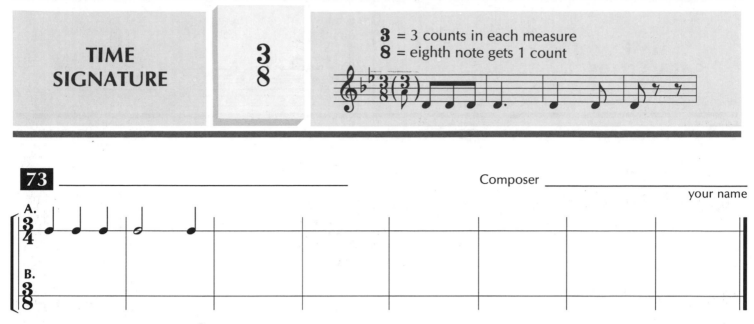

3 = 3 counts in each measure
8 = eighth note gets 1 count

73 _____ Composer _____

your name

► Compose an ending for the ¾ rhythm composition on line **A**. Title your composition, then count and clap it.

► On line **B**, rewrite your composition in ⅜. Count and clap it.

74 TRIPLE PLAY

► Write in the counting and clap the rhythm before you play.

75 WE THREE KINGS

John H. Hopkins, Jr. (1820 - 1891)

► Name the key in "We Three Kings." _____

76 GO FOR EXCELLENCE!

TIME SIGNATURE

6 = 6 counts in each measure
8 = eighth note gets 1 count

77 C MAJOR SCALE SKILL **Page 41**

Andante

▶ This exercise may also be played on drum set.

78 OVER THE RIVER

Traditional

Allegro

▶ Draw in a breath mark ( ) at the end of each phrase.

79 OODLES OF NOODLES

Moderato

80 UPS AND DOWNS

Allegretto

▶ Write in the counting and draw in the bar lines before you play.

81 FOR DRUMS ONLY **Page 41**

Moderato

▶ Play each pattern several times. These patterns may also be played on drum set.

C MAJOR KEY SIGNATURE

This key signature contains no sharps or flats.

TIME SIGNATURE

6 = 6 counts in each measure
8 = eighth note gets 1 count

77 C MAJOR SCALE SKILL   Page 41

Andante
mf

Arpeggio   Chords

78 OVER THE RIVER   Traditional

Allegro
f

1.

2.

▶ Draw in a breath mark (**'**) at the end of each phrase.

79 OODLES OF NOODLES

Moderato
mf

80 UPS AND DOWNS

Allegretto
mp

▶ Write in the counting and draw in the bar lines before you play.

81 FOR MALLETS ONLY

Moderato
mp

82 **WARM-UP - Band Arrangement**

83 **COUNT ME IN**

▶ Write in the counting and clap the rhythm before you play.

84 **KEMO KIMO**

American Folk Song

85 **FRENCH MARCHING SONG**

French Folk Song

86 **FENG YANG SONG**

Chinese Folk Song

87 **GO FOR EXCELLENCE!**

Patrick Gilmore (1829 - 1892)

"When Johnny Comes Marching Home"

SIXTEENTH NOTES

Two sixteenth notes are as long as one eighth note.
Four sixteenth notes are as long as one quarter note.

Each sixteenth note gets $\frac{1}{4}$ count in $\frac{2}{4}$, $\frac{3}{4}$, and $\frac{4}{4}$ time.

82 WARM-UP - Band Arrangement

Andante

mf

83 COUNT ME IN

Moderato

mf

▶ Write in the counting and clap the rhythm before you play.

84 KEMO KIMO

American Folk Song

Allegretto

p   *f*   *p*   *f*

p   *f*

85 FRENCH MARCHING SONG

French Folk Song

Ab   Ab

Allegro

f

1.   2.

▶ Name the interval between the first and second notes. _____

86 FENG YANG SONG   Page 41

Chinese Folk Song

Moderato

mp

87 GO FOR EXCELLENCE!

Patrick Gilmore (1829 - 1892)

Allegro

"When Johnny Comes Marching Home"

mp   *mf*

f   *mp*

SYNCOPATED ROLL IN ₵

88 LOOBY LOO Anonymous

89 THE THUNDERER John Philip Sousa (1854 - 1932)

90 LISTEN TO THE MOCKINGBIRD - Tacet ▶ See "Mallets" page 20.

91 GIVE MY REGARDS TO BROADWAY George M. Cohan (1878 - 1942)

92 FOR SNARE DRUMS ONLY

88 LOOBY LOO

Anonymous

▶ Name the key in "Looby Loo."_____

89 THE THUNDERER

John Philip Sousa (1854 - 1932)

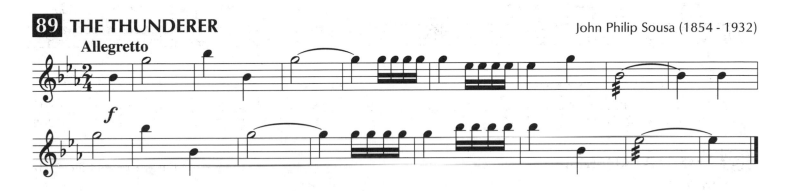

90 LISTEN TO THE MOCKINGBIRD

Alice Hawthorne (1827 - 1902)

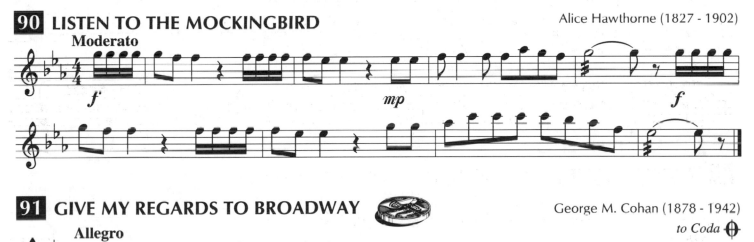

91 GIVE MY REGARDS TO BROADWAY

George M. Cohan (1878 - 1942)

▶ Terminate rolls when the rest of the band cuts off.

92 FOR MALLETS ONLY

93 **CHESTER - Band Arrangement**

William Billings (1746 - 1800)
arr. Bruce Pearson (b. 1942)

94 **STEADY AS YOU GO - Duet**

95 **TIRRA LIRRA LOO**

Canadian Folk Song

96 **GO FOR EXCELLENCE!**

American Folk Song

"Big Rock Candy Mountain"

EIGHTH/SIXTEENTH NOTE COMBINATIONS

William Billings (1746 - 1800)
arr. Bruce Pearson (b. 1942)

93 CHESTER - Band Arrangement

Andante

mf *legato*

p

f

p

94 STEADY AS YOU GO - Duet

Moderato

A.

mf

B.

mf

95 TIRRA LIRRA LOO

Canadian Folk Song

Moderato

f

▶ Write in the counting and clap the rhythm before you play.

96 GO FOR EXCELLENCE!

American Folk Song

Moderato

"Big Rock Candy Mountain"

f

p

f

f

To play with the recorded piano accompaniment, see "Mallets" page 22.

Snare Drum
Bass Drum

TURKISH MARCH
from "The Ruins of Athens"
Percussion Solo or Ensemble

Ludwig van Beethoven (1770 - 1827)
arr. Bruce Pearson (b. 1942)

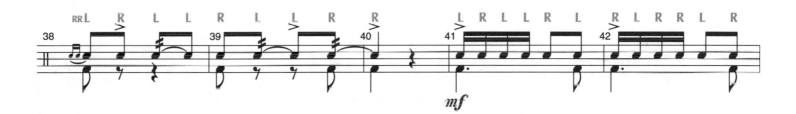

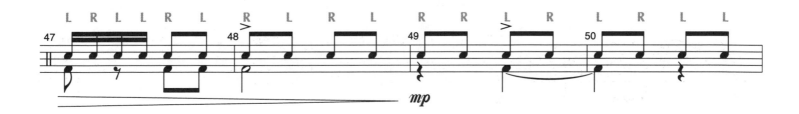

The written piano accompaniment for TURKISH MARCH is included on track 1 of CD 2 for easy access in a performance situation.

TURKISH MARCH
from "The Ruins of Athens"
Percussion Solo or Ensemble

Ludwig van Beethoven (1770 - 1827)
arr. Bruce Pearson (b. 1942)

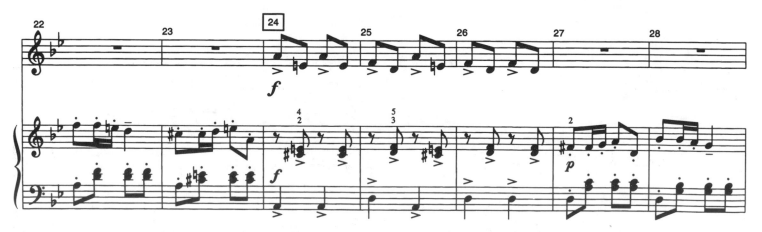

97 BLAZIN'
Moderato

98 AMERICAN PATROL
Frank W. Meacham (1856 - 1909)
Moderato

99 KERRY DANCE
Irish Folk Song
Moderato

100 GAVOTTE
James Hook (1746 - 1827)
Andante

101 FOR DRUMS ONLY
Page 41

Moderato

▶ This exercise may also be played on drum set.

97 **BLAZIN'** Page 41 ▶

▶ Name the interval between the first and second notes. _____

98 **AMERICAN PATROL** Frank W. Meacham (1856 - 1909)

99 **KERRY DANCE** Irish Folk Song

100 **GAVOTTE** James Hook (1746 - 1827)

101 **FOR MALLETS ONLY**

▶ Identify the intervals between the notes before you play.

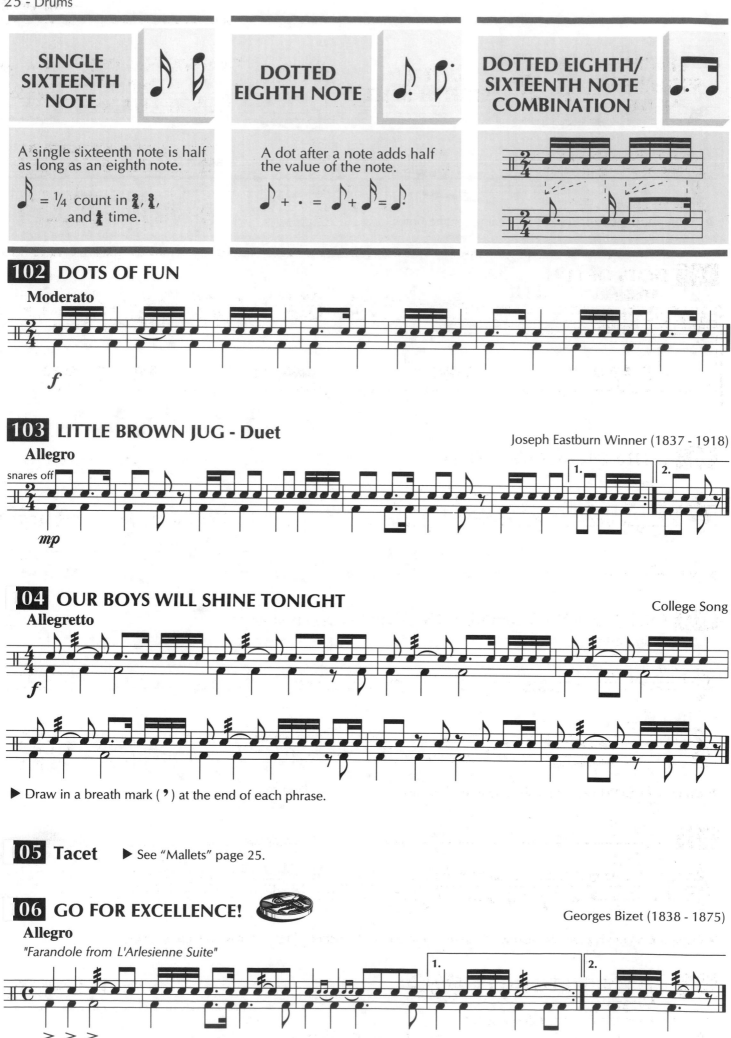

SINGLE SIXTEENTH NOTE

A single sixteenth note is half as long as an eighth note.

♬ = ¼ count in 2/2, 2/4, and 4/4 time.

DOTTED EIGHTH NOTE

A dot after a note adds half the value of the note.

♪ + · = ♪ + ♬ = ♪.

DOTTED EIGHTH/ SIXTEENTH NOTE COMBINATION

102 DOTS OF FUN

Moderato

f

clap

103 LITTLE BROWN JUG - Duet

Joseph Eastburn Winner (1837 - 1918)

Allegro

mp

▶ Write in the counting and clap the rhythm before you play.

104 OUR BOYS WILL SHINE TONIGHT   Page 41 ▏▏▏▏➡   College Song

Allegretto

f

▶ Draw in a breath mark (') at the end of each phrase.

105 _____   Composer _____
                                                                    your name

▶ Compose an ending for this melody. Be sure to use the ♪. ♪ rhythm. Title and play your composition.

106 GO FOR EXCELLENCE!   Georges Bizet (1838 - 1875)

Allegro

"Farandole from L'Arlesienne Suite"

ff

SEVEN STROKE ROLL

The seven stroke roll is a Rudiment.

107 **CUCKOO SONG - Tacet** ▶ See "Mallets" page 26.

08 **MARCH MILITAIRE**

Franz Schubert (1797 - 1828)

Allegretto

to Coda ⊕

D.C. al Coda   ⊕ *Coda*

09 **ST. ANTHONY CHORALE**

Franz Joseph Haydn (1732 - 1809)

Andante

snares off

1.   2.   *Fine*

D.C. al Fine

110 **Tacet**   ▶ See "Mallets" page 26.

111 **FOR SNARE DRUMS ONLY**   Page 41 ⦀⇒

A   Moderato

B

▶ Try playing this exercise using multiple bounce strokes (𝄽) rather than open double strokes (♩).

107 **CUCKOO SONG**

Austrian Folk Song

108 **MARCH MILITAIRE**

Franz Schubert (1797 - 1828)

109 **ST. ANTHONY CHORALE** Page 41 ▐▐▐▐➤

Franz Joseph Haydn (1732 - 1809)

110 _____ Composer _____

your name

▶ Arrange these melodic pieces in any order to build a tune you like. You may use pieces more than once. Title and play your composition.

111 **FOR MALLETS ONLY**

EIGHTH NOTE TRIPLET

$\frac{1}{3} + \frac{1}{3} + \frac{1}{3} = \frac{2}{3} + \frac{1}{3} = 1$ count in $\frac{2}{4}$, $\frac{3}{4}$, and $\frac{4}{4}$ time.

TEMPO

Maestoso - majestically

112 TRIPLE TREAT

Moderato

113 STARS OF THE HEAVENS - Duet Page 41 Mexican Folk Song

Allegro

114 LIGHT CAVALRY OVERTURE Franz von Suppé (1819 - 1895)

Maestoso

115 GO FOR EXCELLENCE! Charles Gounod (1818 - 1893)

Maestoso

"Soldiers' Chorus from Faust"

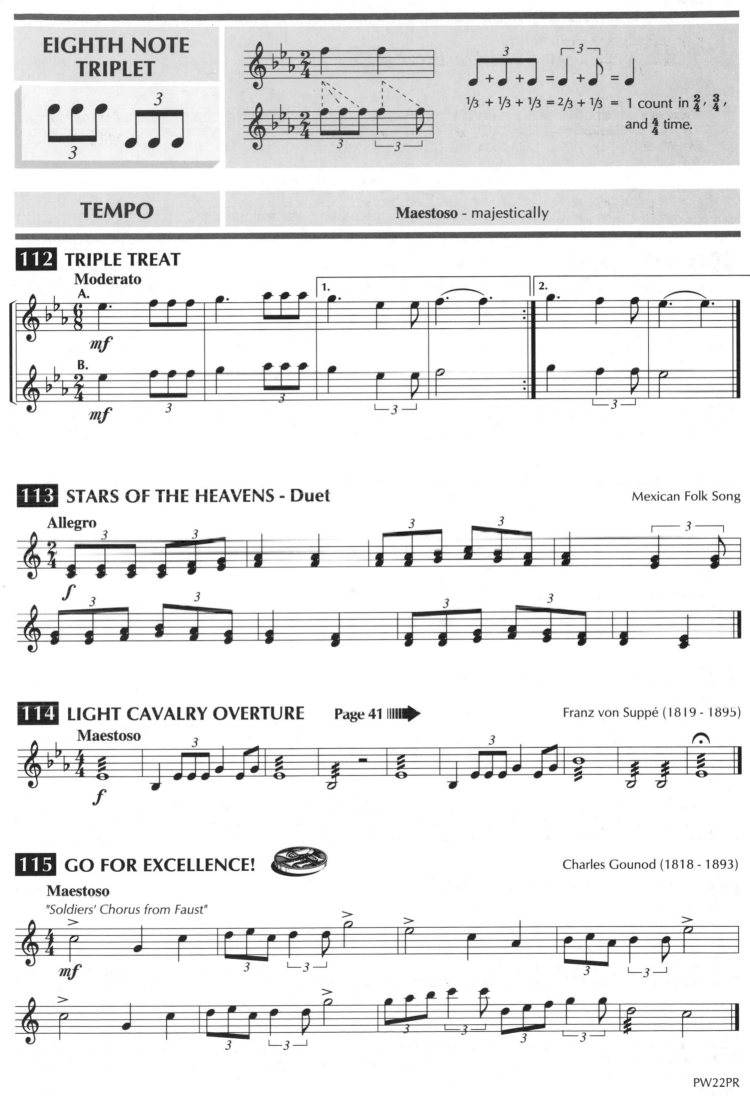

116 HERE WE COME A-WASSAILING

English Folk Song

117 THEME FROM "ZAMPA"

Ferdinand Herold (1791 - 1833)

118 GO FOR EXCELLENCE!

Peter Ilyich Tchaikovsky (1840 - 1893)

Allegretto

"March from the Nutcracker"

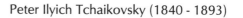

116 HERE WE COME A-WASSAILING — English Folk Song

117 THEME FROM "ZAMPA" — Ferdinand Herold (1791 - 1833)

118 GO FOR EXCELLENCE! — Peter Ilyich Tchaikovsky (1840 - 1893)
"March from the Nutcracker"

CABO RICO
Band Arrangement

Chuck Elledge (b. 1961)

CABO RICO
Band Arrangement

Bells

Chuck Elledge (b. 1961)

RUDIMENTAL REGIMENT

Band Arrangement

Bruce Pearson (b. 1942)
and Chuck Elledge (b. 1961)

Snare Drum
Bass Drum

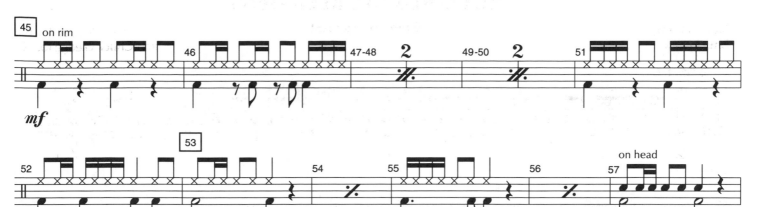

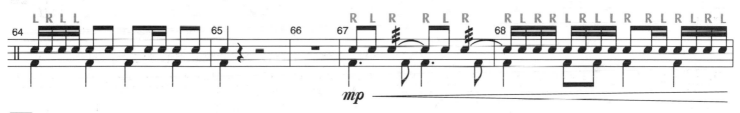

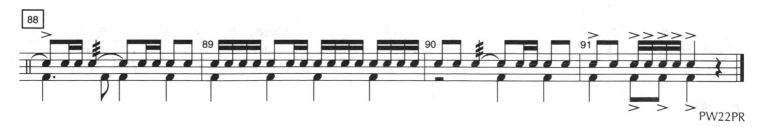

RUDIMENTAL REGIMENT
Band Arrangement

Bells

Bruce Pearson (b. 1942)
and Chuck Elledge (b. 1961)

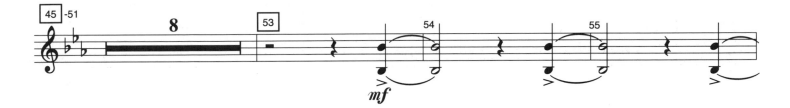

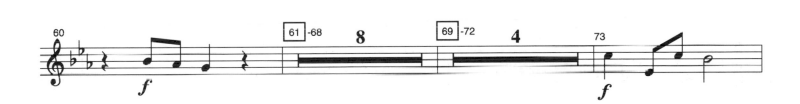

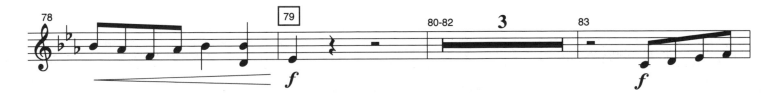

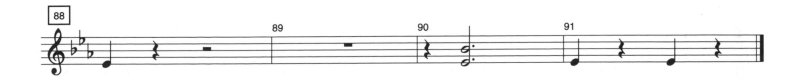

SUMMER'S RAIN

Band Arrangement

Chuck Elledge (b. 1961)

▶ The S. Cym. and S.D. parts should be played by one percussionist. Advanced percussionists may also try playing all parts, including the B.D. part, on drum set.

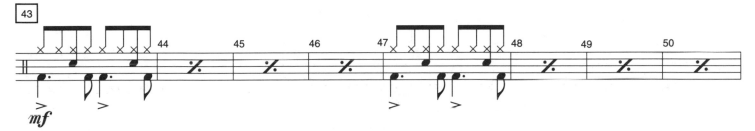

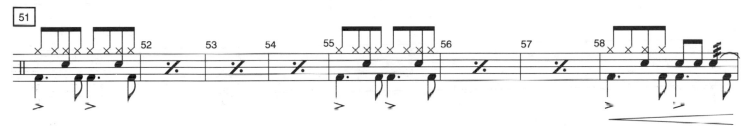

SUMMER'S RAIN
Band Arrangement

Bells

Chuck Elledge (b. 1961)

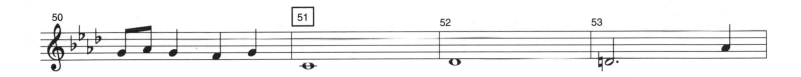

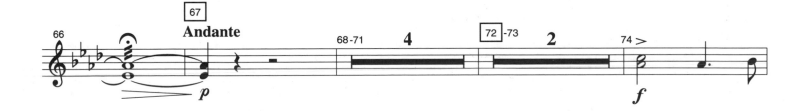

FRENCH MARKET BUZZARDS MARCH

Band Arrangement

Liberato Gallo
arr. Wendy Barden (b. 1955)

Snare Drum
Bass Drum

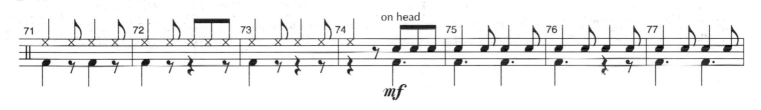

D.S. al Fine

FRENCH MARKET BUZZARDS MARCH
Band Arrangement

Liberato Gallo
arr. Wendy Barden (b. 1955)

Bells

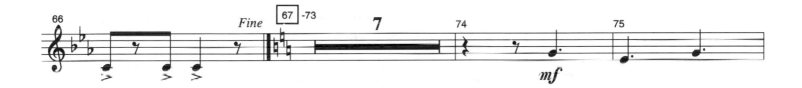

JAMAICAN SUNRISE

Percussion Ensemble

Bruce Pearson (b. 1942)

Snare Drum
Bass Drum

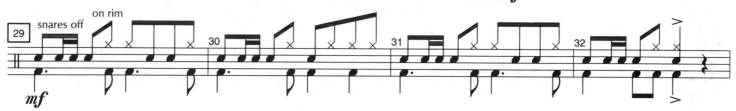

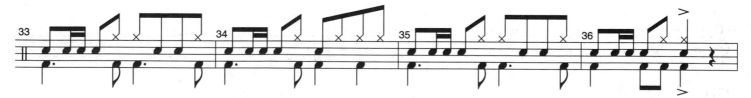

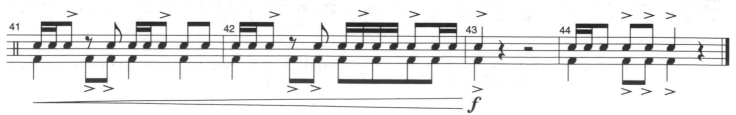

PW22PR

JAMAICAN SUNRISE
Percussion Ensemble

Bruce Pearson (b. 1942)

▶ This part may also be played on bells or xylophone if a marimba is not available. Use plastic mallets when playing bells, and hard rubber mallets when playing xylophone. For more information, see "Mallets" page 48.

ARKANSAS TRAVELER

Percussion Ensemble

Traditional
arr. Bruce Pearson (b. 1942)

Snare Drum
Bass Drum

Hey!

ARKANSAS TRAVELER

Percussion Ensemble

Traditional
arr. Bruce Pearson (b. 1942)

Bells and **Xylophone**

Moderato

(with hard plastic mallets)

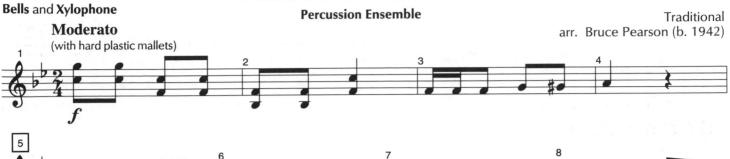

Hey!

▶ For more information on the xylophone, see "Mallets" page 48.

DRUMS ALA RONDO
Snare Drum/Bass Drum Duet

Bruce Pearson (b. 1942)

▶ A rondo is a piece of music in which presentations of the main theme ("A") are separated by contrasting themes ("B," "C," etc.). The form of this rondo is "A - B - A - C - A." Before you play, identify the measures at which each section of the rondo begins.

EXPRESS LANE

Multiple Percussion Solo

Bruce Pearson (b. 1942)

▶ This solo should be played by one percussionist. Set-up the instruments as shown in the diagram at the top of the page. Adjust the exact position of each instrument and the music stand so that the set-up is comfortable for you.
▶ Use medium weight S.D. sticks when playing this solo.
▶ To play the Tamb. with sticks, place it head side down on a soft, flat surface and strike it lightly on the rim.
▶ If Tom-toms are not available, use two snare drums with snares off, one tuned higher than the other.

The written piano accompaniment for
MAPLE LEAF RAG is included on track 14
of CD 2. You will hear a 2-measure click
before you play to help you get started.

MAPLE LEAF RAG
Solo with Piano Accompaniment

Scott Joplin (1868 - 1917)
arr. Bruce Pearson (b. 1942)

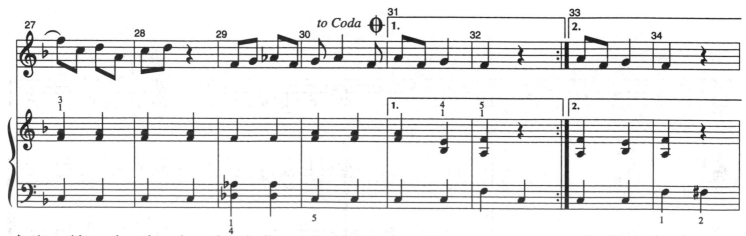

▶ If possible, perform this solo on the xylophone, using hard plastic mallets.

EXCELLERATORS - FOR DRUMS ONLY

► Practice this exercise two ways: 1. Beginning with the right hand; 2. Beginning with the left hand.

► These patterns should be played on drum set. Play each pattern several times without stopping. Practice all possible two limb combinations (S. Cym. & S.D., S. Cym. and B.D., S.D. and B.D.) before playing each pattern as written.

EXCELLERATORS - FOR DRUMS ONLY

▶ Practice this exercise two ways: 1. Beginning with the right hand; 2. Beginning with the left hand.

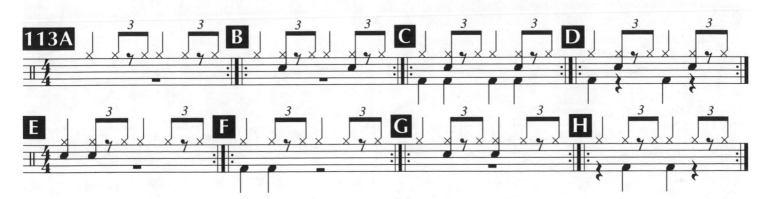

EXCELLERATORS - FOR MALLETS ONLY

▶ Write in the sticking that works best for you.

EXCELLERATORS - FOR MALLETS ONLY

▶ Write in the sticking that works best for you.

▶ Try a variety of stickings.

STICKING STUDIES (SCALE STUDIES)

B♭ MAJOR SCALE

G HARMONIC MINOR SCALE

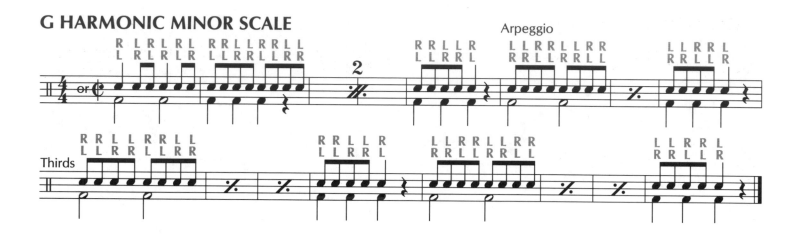

E♭ MAJOR SCALE

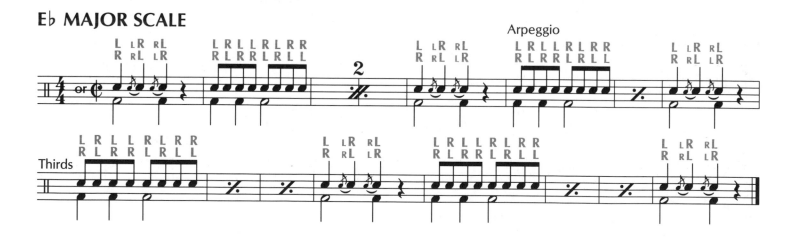

C HARMONIC MINOR SCALE

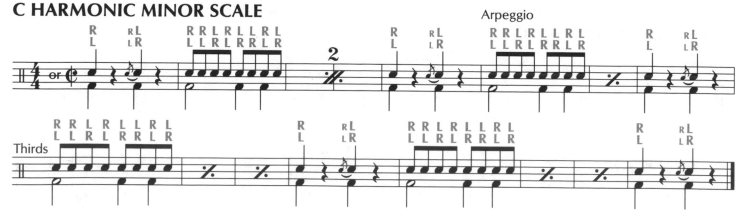

SCALE STUDIES

Bb MAJOR SCALE

▶ When scales appear in octaves, practice them three ways: 1. Play upper octave only; 2. Play lower octave only; 3. Play as double stops.

G HARMONIC MINOR SCALE

Eb MAJOR SCALE

C HARMONIC MINOR SCALE

STICKING STUDIES (SCALE STUDIES)

F MAJOR SCALE

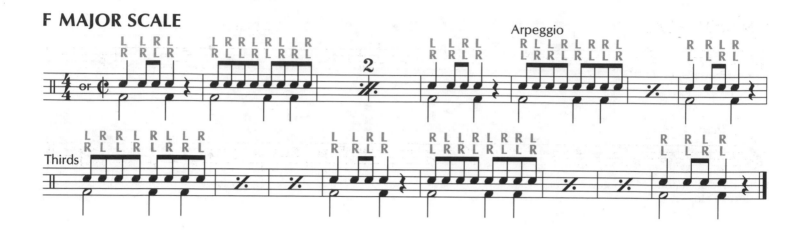

A♭ MAJOR SCALE

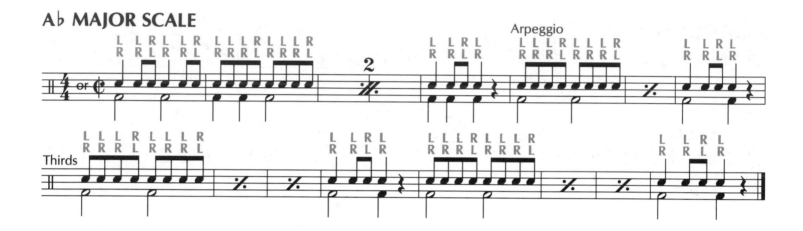

C MAJOR SCALE

CHROMATIC SCALE

SCALE STUDIES

F MAJOR SCALE

Arpeggio

Thirds

Ab MAJOR SCALE

Arpeggio

Thirds

C MAJOR SCALE

Arpeggio

Thirds

CHROMATIC SCALE

RHYTHM STUDIES

RHYTHM STUDIES

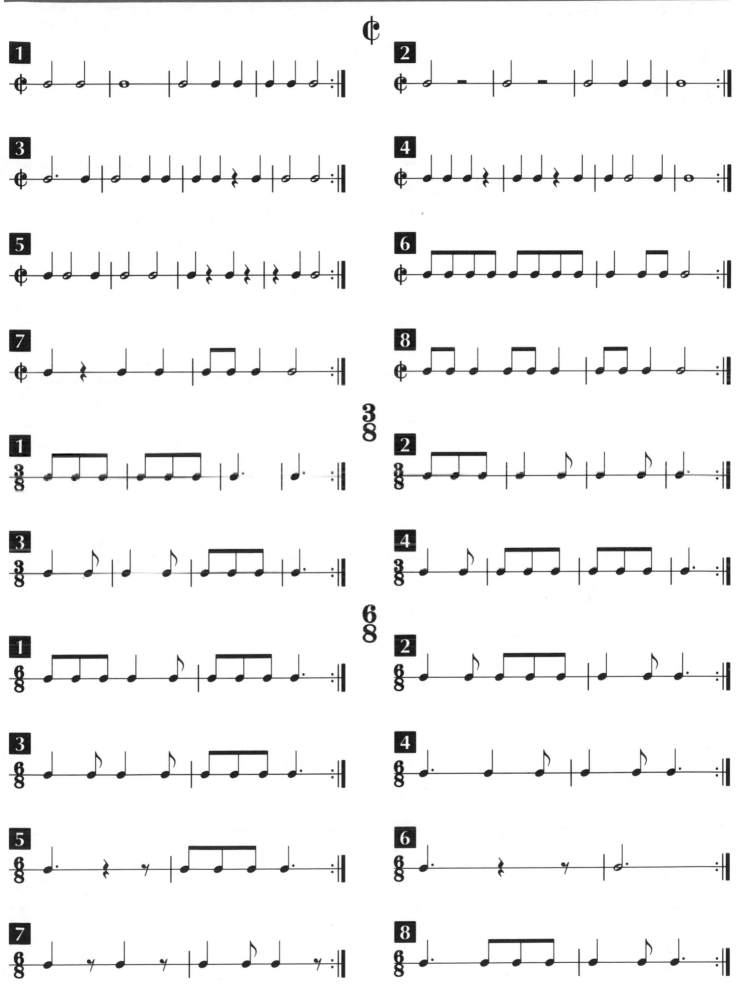

GLOSSARY/INDEX

▶ D = Drum page, M = Mallet page

Multiple Bounce Stroke (p.2D) . . . . type of stroke that produces
three or more sounds (hits)
with a single wrist movement;
the first hit is the strongest,
with the others gradually
decreasing in intensity

Multiple Bounce Stroke Roll (pp.2D, 48D) . drum roll played using multiple
bounce strokes; used for most
concert band, orchestra, and
ensemble playing; also called
buzz roll, press roll, closed
roll, concert roll, and
orchestral roll

Nine Stroke Roll (Quarter Note Roll)
(pp.2D, 6D, 48D) . . . . a Rudiment; when played using
open double strokes, a total
of 9 strokes are produced

On Rim (pp.8D, 12D, 22-23D, 31D, 34-
37D) . . . . an instruction to play the drum
part on the drum rim instead
of the drum head

Open Double Stroke (p.2D) . . . . type of stroke that produces
two sounds (hits) with a single
wrist movement; both hits
should sound the same

Orchestra Bells (see **Bells**)
Orchestral Roll (see **Multiple Bounce
Stroke Roll**)
Paradiddle, Double (see **Double
Paradiddle**)
Pearson, Bruce . . . . American music educator/
composer/arranger (b. 1942)
Polyphony (p.9M) . . . . two or more melodies played at
the same time

Press Roll (see **Multiple Bounce Stroke
Roll**)
Quarter Note Roll (see **Nine Stroke Roll**)
R.S. (see **Rim Shot**)
Resonator (Resonating Tube) (p.48M) . . . . . on a mallet instrument, a tube
which naturally amplifies the
volume and enriches the
sound of a vibrating bar after
the bar is struck

Rim Shot (R.S.) (pp.8D, 16D, 32D, 37D) . . . special effect played on a drum;
to create, place the tip of one
stick on the drum head; strike
the shaft of that stick with the
shaft of the other stick

Rudiments (pp.2-4D, 6D, 8D, 10D, 14D,
26D, 48D) . . . . 40 basic techniques and
sticking patterns used in snare
drum playing
Schubert, Franz (p.26) . . . . Austrian composer (1797-1828)
Seven Stroke Roll (p.26D) . . . . a Rudiment; when played using
open double strokes, a total
of 7 strokes are produced

 or

Seventeen Stroke Roll (Half Note Roll)
(pp.4D, 48D) . . . . a Rudiment; when played using
open double strokes, a total
of 17 strokes are produced

Single Drag Tap (pp.10D, 48D) . . . . a Rudiment; consists of a drag
followed by an accented stroke
played by the opposite hand

Snares Off (pp.3D, 7-8D, 10-11D, 13D,
16-17D, 19D, 25-27D, 29D, 36D) . . . . an instruction to move the snare
release lever so snares are not
touching the snare head
Sousa, John Philip (pp.13, 15, 20) . . . . American composer (1854-1932)
Suppé, Franz von (p.27) . . . . Belgian composer (1819-1895)
Suspended Cymbal (see **Cymbal,
Suspended**)
Syncopation (pp.5, 6D, 20D) . . . . a rhythmic effect which places
emphasis on a weak or
unaccented part of the measure

**Syncopated Nine Stroke Roll (Syncopated
Quarter Note Roll)** (p.6D) . . . . nine stroke roll (quarter note roll)
played on the weak or unac-
cented part of the measure

Syncopated Quarter Note Roll (see
Syncopated Nine Stroke Roll)
Tacet (p.2D) . . . . do not play
Tambourine (p.39D) . . . . hand-held drum with a single head
and jingles attached to its shell
Tchaikovsky, Peter Ilyich (pp.11, 28) . . . . . . Russian composer (1840-1893)
Texture (p.12M) . . . . the character of a composition as
determined by the relationship of
its melodies, countermelodies,
and/or chords
Tom-tom (p.39D) . . . . single or double headed drum
without snares; played with snare
drum sticks, felt mallets, or yarn
mallets

Tubular Bells (see **Chimes**)
Vibes (see **Vibraphone**)
Vibraharp (see **Vibraphone**)
Vibraphone (p.48M) . . . . mallet percussion instrument with
metal bars, a resonating tube
under each bar, a damper pedal,
and a motor-rotated disk in each
resonator which creates a vibrato
effect; also called vibes or
vibraharp

Winner, Joseph Eastburn (p.25) . . . . American composer (1837-1918)
Xylophone (pp.37-39M, 48M) . . . . mallet percussion instrument with
wooden or synthetic bars, and
usually a resonating tube under
each bar

STANDARD OF EXCELLENCE

EXERCISE 2
- [ ] rhythm
- [ ] 9 stroke rolls
- [ ] grip
- [ ] B.D. tech.

EXERCISE 12
- [ ] rhythm
- [ ] pulse
- [ ] rolls
- [ ] 2-meas. repeat

EXERCISE 28
- [ ] rhythm
- [ ] double parad.
- [ ] posture
- [ ] grip

EXERCISE 36
- [ ] rhythm
- [ ] drag
- [ ] paradiddles
- [ ] accents

EXERCISE 47
- [ ] rhythm
- [ ] single drag tap
- [ ] flam parads.
- [ ] long roll

EXERCISE 62
- [ ] rhythm
- [ ] flams
- [ ] dynamics
- [ ] accents

EXERCISE 72
- [ ] rhythm
- [ ] pulse
- [ ] coordination
- [ ] posture

EXERCISE 87
- [ ] rhythm
- [ ] dynamics
- [ ] accents
- [ ] B.D. tech.

EXERCISE 96
- [ ] rhythm
- [ ] rolls
- [ ] dynamics
- [ ] accents

EXERCISE 111
- [ ] rhythm
- [ ] pulse
- [ ] 7 stroke rolls
- [ ] grip

EXERCISE 5
- [ ] rhythm
- [ ] paradiddles
- [ ] dynamics
- [ ] *D.C. al Fine*

EXERCISE 16
- [ ] rhythm
- [ ] long roll
- [ ] 𝄒
- [ ] grip

EXERCISE 29
- [ ] rhythm
- [ ] double parads.
- [ ] flam accents
- [ ] *D.C. al Fine*

EXERCISE 39
- [ ] rhythm
- [ ] sticking
- [ ] dynamics
- [ ] *accelerando*

EXERCISE 51
- [ ] 5 stroke rolls
- [ ] flam taps
- [ ] double parad.
- [ ] drags

EXERCISE 65
- [ ] rhythm
- [ ] flams
- [ ] rolls
- [ ] *D.C. al Fine*

EXERCISE 76
- [ ] rhythm
- [ ] pulse
- [ ] flam accent
- [ ] tempo

EXERCISE 88
- [ ] rhythm
- [ ] pulse
- [ ] B.D. tech.
- [ ] time signatures

EXERCISE 100
- [ ] rhythm
- [ ] flamacues
- [ ] single drag taps
- [ ] dynamics

EXERCISE 115
- [ ] rhythm
- [ ] pulse
- [ ] tempo
- [ ] posture

EXERCISE 6
- [ ] rhythm
- [ ] 5 stroke rolls
- [ ] grip
- [ ] B.D. tech.

EXERCISE 21
- [ ] rhythm
- [ ] pulse
- [ ] posture
- [ ] grip

EXERCISE 33
- [ ] rhythm
- [ ] double parads.
- [ ] flam parads.
- [ ] dynamics

EXERCISE 42
- [ ] rhythm
- [ ] snares off
- [ ] long roll
- [ ] time signatures

EXERCISE 53
- [ ] rhythm
- [ ] pulse
- [ ] drags
- [ ] sync. 9 stk. roll

EXERCISE 67
- [ ] rhythm
- [ ] flamacue
- [ ] posture
- [ ] repeat

EXERCISE 77
- [ ] rhythm
- [ ] pulse
- [ ] coordination
- [ ] posture

EXERCISE 91
- [ ] rhythm
- [ ] pulse
- [ ] rolls in ¢
- [ ] *D.C. al Coda*

EXERCISE 101
- [ ] rhythm
- [ ] posture
- [ ] coordination
- [ ] 1st/2nd endings

EXERCISE 116
- [ ] rhythm
- [ ] time signatures
- [ ] flams
- [ ] 2-meas. repeat

EXERCISE 7
- [ ] rhythm
- [ ] *ritardando*
- [ ] dynamics
- [ ] 1st/2nd endings

EXERCISE 24
- [ ] rhythm
- [ ] flam tap
- [ ] rolls
- [ ] 𝄒

EXERCISE 35
- [ ] rhythm
- [ ] posture
- [ ] grip
- [ ] drags

EXERCISE 45
- [ ] rhythm
- [ ] pulse
- [ ] coordination
- [ ] posture

EXERCISE 57
- [ ] rhythm
- [ ] posture
- [ ] coordination
- [ ] 1st/2nd endings

EXERCISE 69
- [ ] rhythm
- [ ] pulse
- [ ] rolls
- [ ] dynamics

EXERCISE 81
- [ ] rhythm
- [ ] pulse
- [ ] coordination
- [ ] posture

EXERCISE 92
- [ ] flam parads.
- [ ] flamacue
- [ ] flam accents
- [ ] single drag taps

EXERCISE 106
- [ ] rhythm
- [ ] rolls
- [ ] drags
- [ ] B.D. tech.

EXERCISE 118
- [ ] rhythm
- [ ] drags
- [ ] B.D. tech.
- [ ] tempo

EXCELLENCE

Use this chart to record your progress on the "Drums" pages.

STANDARD OF EXCELLENCE

EXERCISE 2
- [ ] notes/rhythm
- [ ] rolls
- [ ] double stops
- [ ] grip

EXERCISE 5
- [ ] notes/rhythm
- [ ] rolls
- [ ] dynamics
- [ ] *D.C. al Fine*

EXERCISE 6
- [ ] notes/rhythm
- [ ] rolls
- [ ] double stops
- [ ] hand position

EXERCISE 7
- [ ] notes/rhythm
- [ ] *ritardando*
- [ ] dynamics
- [ ] 1st/2nd endings

EXERCISE 12
- [ ] notes/rhythm
- [ ] rolls
- [ ] double stops
- [ ] posture

EXERCISE 16
- [ ] notes/rhythm
- [ ] rolls
- [ ] sticking
- [ ] stroke

EXERCISE 21
- [ ] notes/rhythm
- [ ] rolls
- [ ] dynamics
- [ ] tempo

EXERCISE 24
- [ ] notes/rhythm
- [ ] pulse
- [ ] ⌒
- [ ] stroke

EXERCISE 28
- [ ] notes/rhythm
- [ ] rolls
- [ ] double stops
- [ ] tempo

EXERCISE 29
- [ ] notes/rhythm
- [ ] rolls
- [ ] grip
- [ ] *D.C. al Fine*

EXERCISE 33
- [ ] notes/rhythm
- [ ] pulse
- [ ] sticking
- [ ] dynamics

EXERCISE 35
- [ ] notes/rhythm
- [ ] sticking
- [ ] posture
- [ ] hand position

EXERCISE 36
- [ ] notes/rhythm
- [ ] rolls
- [ ] double stops
- [ ] stroke

EXERCISE 39
- [ ] notes/rhythm
- [ ] rolls
- [ ] dynamics
- [ ] *accelerando*

EXERCISE 42
- [ ] notes/rhythm
- [ ] rolls
- [ ] time signatures
- [ ] ⌒

EXERCISE 45
- [ ] notes/rhythm
- [ ] sticking
- [ ] rolls
- [ ] double stops

EXERCISE 47
- [ ] notes/rhythm
- [ ] posture
- [ ] grip
- [ ] stroke

EXERCISE 51
- [ ] notes/rhythm
- [ ] pulse
- [ ] sticking
- [ ] tempo

EXERCISE 53
- [ ] notes/rhythm
- [ ] pulse
- [ ] rolls
- [ ] tempo

EXERCISE 57
- [ ] notes/rhythm
- [ ] pulse
- [ ] coordination
- [ ] repeat

EXERCISE 62
- [ ] notes/rhythm
- [ ] sticking
- [ ] dynamics
- [ ] tempo

EXERCISE 65
- [ ] notes/rhythm
- [ ] sticking
- [ ] posture
- [ ] *D.C. al Fine*

EXERCISE 67
- [ ] notes/rhythm
- [ ] hand position
- [ ] grip
- [ ] stroke

EXERCISE 69
- [ ] notes/rhythm
- [ ] sticking
- [ ] dynamics
- [ ] posture

EXERCISE 72
- [ ] notes/rhythm
- [ ] pulse
- [ ] rolls
- [ ] sticking

EXERCISE 76
- [ ] notes/rhythm
- [ ] rolls
- [ ] sticking
- [ ] tempo

EXERCISE 77
- [ ] notes/rhythm
- [ ] double stops
- [ ] hand position
- [ ] tempo

EXERCISE 81
- [ ] notes/rhythm
- [ ] rolls
- [ ] double stops
- [ ] posture

EXERCISE 87
- [ ] notes/rhythm
- [ ] sticking
- [ ] dynamics
- [ ] tempo

EXERCISE 88
- [ ] notes/rhythm
- [ ] pulse
- [ ] rolls
- [ ] time signatures

EXERCISE 91
- [ ] notes/rhythm
- [ ] pulse
- [ ] rolls
- [ ] *D.C. al Coda*

EXERCISE 92
- [ ] notes/rhythm
- [ ] rolls
- [ ] double stops
- [ ] tempo

EXERCISE 96
- [ ] notes/rhythm
- [ ] sticking
- [ ] dynamics
- [ ] accents

EXERCISE 100
- [ ] notes/rhythm
- [ ] sticking
- [ ] dynamics
- [ ] tempo

EXERCISE 101
- [ ] notes/rhythm
- [ ] pulse
- [ ] hand position
- [ ] interval I.D.

EXERCISE 106
- [ ] notes/rhythm
- [ ] rolls
- [ ] tempo
- [ ] grip

EXERCISE 111
- [ ] notes/rhythm
- [ ] rolls
- [ ] articulation
- [ ] stroke

EXERCISE 115
- [ ] notes/rhythm
- [ ] sticking
- [ ] tempo
- [ ] accents

EXERCISE 116
- [ ] notes/rhythm
- [ ] pulse
- [ ] time signatures
- [ ] tempo

EXERCISE 118
- [ ] notes/rhythm
- [ ] pulse
- [ ] sticking
- [ ] tempo

EXCELLENCE

Use this chart to record your progress on the "Mallets" pages.

PERCUSSIVE ARTS SOCIETY
INTERNATIONAL DRUM RUDIMENTS

▶ All Rudiments should be practiced: *open* (slow) to *close* (fast) to *open* (slow) and/or at an even, moderate march tempo.

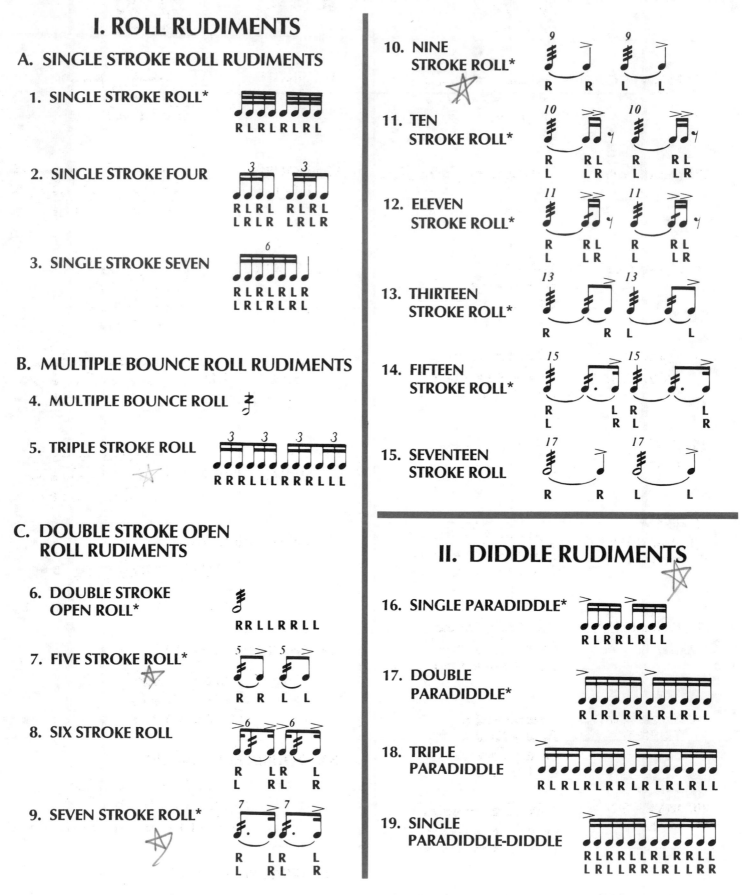

I. ROLL RUDIMENTS

A. SINGLE STROKE ROLL RUDIMENTS

1. SINGLE STROKE ROLL*
2. SINGLE STROKE FOUR
3. SINGLE STROKE SEVEN

B. MULTIPLE BOUNCE ROLL RUDIMENTS

4. MULTIPLE BOUNCE ROLL
5. TRIPLE STROKE ROLL

C. DOUBLE STROKE OPEN ROLL RUDIMENTS

6. DOUBLE STROKE OPEN ROLL*
7. FIVE STROKE ROLL*
8. SIX STROKE ROLL
9. SEVEN STROKE ROLL*

10. NINE STROKE ROLL*
11. TEN STROKE ROLL*
12. ELEVEN STROKE ROLL*
13. THIRTEEN STROKE ROLL*
14. FIFTEEN STROKE ROLL*
15. SEVENTEEN STROKE ROLL

II. DIDDLE RUDIMENTS

16. SINGLE PARADIDDLE*
17. DOUBLE PARADIDDLE*
18. TRIPLE PARADIDDLE
19. SINGLE PARADIDDLE-DIDDLE

*These Rudiments are also included in the original Standard 26 American Drum Rudiments.

III. FLAM RUDIMENTS

20. FLAM*

L R   R L

21. FLAM ACCENT*

L R L R   R L R L

22. FLAM TAP*

L R R R L L   L R R R L L

23. FLAMACUE*

L R L R L L R
R L R L R R L

24. FLAM PARADIDDLE*

L R L R R   R L R L L

25. SINGLE FLAMMED MILL

L R R L R R L L R L

26. FLAM PARADIDDLE-DIDDLE*

L R L R R R L L R L R L L R R

27. PATAFLAFLA

L R L R R L L R L R R L

28. SWISS ARMY TRIPLET

L R R L L R R L
R L L L R R L L R

29. INVERTED FLAM TAP

L R L R L R L R L L R

30. FLAM DRAG

L R L L R   R L R R L

IV. DRAG RUDIMENTS

31. DRAG*

LL R   RR L

32. SINGLE DRAG TAP*

LL R L   RR L R

33. DOUBLE DRAG TAP*

LL R LL R L   RR L RR L R

34. LESSON 25*

LL R L R L   LL R L R L
RR L R L R   RR L R L R

35. SINGLE DRAGADIDDLE

RR L R R L   LL R L L

36. DRAG PARADIDDLE #1*

R LL R L R R L   RR L R L L

37. DRAG PARADIDDLE #2*

R LL R LL R L R R L   RR L RR L R L L

38. SINGLE RATAMACUE*

LL R L R L   RR L R L R

39. DOUBLE RATAMACUE*

LL R LL R L R L   RR L RR L R L R

40. TRIPLE RATAMACUE*

LL R LL R LL R L R L   RR L RR L RR L R L R

MALLET PERCUSSION INSTRUMENTS

There are many different types of mallet percussion instruments. The exercises in this book can be played on any of the mallet instruments shown below.

Bells (also called a **glockenspiel** or **orchestra bells**) have metal bars and are played with hard plastic, rubber, or wood mallets.

BELLS

The **marimba** has wooden bars and a resonating tube under each bar. It is played with soft or medium yarn or rubber mallets.

MARIMBA

XYLOPHONE

The **xylophone** has wooden or synthetic bars. It usually also has a resonating tube under each bar. The xylophone is played with rubber, plastic, or wood mallets.

CHIMES

VIBRAPHONE

Chimes (also called **tubular bells**) are long hanging metal tubes, usually supported on a frame. Most sets of chimes also have a damper pedal, used to control ringing. Chimes are played with rawhide, wood, plastic, or hard rubber hammers.

The **vibraphone** (also called **vibes** or **vibraharp**) has metal bars and a resonating tube under each bar. It also has a damper pedal to control the ringing of the bars, and a motor-rotated disk in each resonator which can be used to create a pulsating, vibrato effect. The vibraphone is usually played with rubber or yarn mallets.